Animal

In Flood and Swiftwater Incidents

by Slim Ray

FLOODFIGHTERS™ series

Animal Rescue
In Flood and Swiftwater Incidents

Cover: An HSUS Disaster Relief Team member helps a
thirsty dog rescued from the Great Flood of 1993.
(HSUS/ Dantzler)

Text, illustrations, and photos by Slim Ray unless otherwise
noted. Book design by Purple Planet Studios.

Library of Congress Catalog No: 99-93280

ISBN 0-9649585-2-X

Produced and distributed by CFS Press
68 Finalee Avenue
Asheville, NC 28803
(828) 253-9102
fax (828) 252-9560
www.cfspress.com
info@cfspress.com

Printed and bound in USA by Keen Impressions

02 01 00 99   6 5 4 3 2 1

Quantity discounts are available on bulk purchases to Fire,
EMS, Animal Welfare and other professional and public service organizations for educational and training purposes. For
more information contact the publisher at the above address.

Animal Rescue
In Flood and Swiftwater Incidents
FLOODFIGHTERS™ series

Table of Contents

WARNING!

Swiftwater rescue is an extremely hazardous activity. You cannot learn swiftwater rescue from a book or a video, no matter how good. There is no substitute for professional training and experience. It is your responsibility to get professional, hands-on training in these areas before attempting to use the techniques and equipment described in this guide in an actual rescue. All techniques in this guide should be thoroughly practiced in a safe environment before they are attempted under field conditions. Even so, there remains a risk of death or serious injury when using them. *This risk must be accepted by the reader/rescuer.* Neither the author nor publisher assumes any responsibility or liability for death or personal injury resulting from the use or misuse of information contained in this book. Swiftwater rescue is a dynamic field. New techniques, equipment, and materials will become available that cannot be discussed in this guide, nor does this guide attempt to cover every conceivable technique or situation. It is the responsibility of the reader to remain abreast of new developments in the field.

Animal Rescue
In Flood and Swiftwater Incidents
FLOODFIGHTERS™ series

Foreword

Animal rescue and swiftwater rescue have been the focus of increasing attention during the past decade. Animal rescue can be more complicated than rescue of humans for many reasons. The biggest hurdle and potential danger (to both handlers and the animals themselves) is in communicating with animals and understanding how they may behave when frightened or stressed. Next, animals present specific hazards of two kinds: physical danger (biting or kicking), and health hazards (disease transmission). As in any rescue of humans, the safety of the rescuers must be considered before the rescue is begun.

Rescue personnel, veterinarians, and animal handlers must work together, sharing their knowledge and skills to best effect rescue. Each individual brings strengths to the team: veterinarians with knowledge of animal behavior, disease transmission, and other animal-associated hazards; animal handlers with their ability to work safely around animals; and rescue personnel with their knowledge of moving water and how it affects the approach to a successful rescue.

Slim Ray's impressive swiftwater rescue knowledge and experience make him the obvious person to address these subjects in one book. Slim has authored several books, including Swiftwater Rescue: A Manual for the Rescue Professional, and River Rescue, considered the standard references on river safety and rescue.

I was a recreational kayaker when I first met Slim, but I'd read his book and was thrilled to accompany this "guru of river rescue" down the Box Canyon of the Rio Grande near Taos, New Mexico. We have kept in touch over the years because of a mutual love for writing and for the water. Slim influenced me to maintain my knowledge of swiftwater rescue for my own personal safety, as well as the safety of my fellow kayakers. When Slim came up with the idea for this book, I knew he'd approach it with the same thoroughness and care that he used with his other books.

In Swiftwater Animal Rescue he expertly ties together information about animal behavior, hazards associated with animals, and the specific factors that are involved in water rescue. Each of those subjects could, in itself, fill an entire book; professionals involved with animal rescue should consider this book as an educational backgrounder from which they can build their knowledge of animal handling, reduction of the dangers associated with animals, and rescues that take place in standing or moving water.

Carin A. Smith, DVM
Smith Veterinary Services
Leavenworth, Washington

Introduction

Why animal rescue?

To some people this will seem obvious, but if you are fire-fighter or other emergency services worker, it may not. "We got better things to do than rescue grandma's cat," if the often heard refrain. However, the public knows that firefighters do two things—put out fires and rescue cats from trees. So animal rescue is part of the job, at least in the public's mind, whether we like it or not.

Consider:

• Approximately 50% of all U.S. households have a pet of some kind. (see Appendix G for pet population estimates)
• Livestock losses in floods can often be measured in millions of dollars. While pet drownings are fairly rare, large numbers of cattle have perished in floods. "[F]looding killed several thousand dairy cows in the 1991 Snohomish Valley, Washington, floods; 1200 dairy cows in Tilamook, Oregon, in 1996; and approximately 90,000 beef cows in the Dakotas and Minnesota in 1997." (Heath 1999)

The most compelling reason, however, is that the rescue of people and animals is tied together and can't be separated. People often refuse to evacuate without their pets, even if the evacuation is mandatory. One study of the 1997 floods in Marysville, CA, showed that while the overall evacuation rate was about 80%, just under 80% of those who did *not* evacuate owned pets. (Heath 1999) Seniors, especially, are reluctant to evacuate without their pets, since these may be "family."

Reluctance to evacuate is higher for pet owners without children. The likelihood of non-evacuation approximately doubles for these owners with each additional pet. (Heath 1999) Heath also notes that "approximately 20% to 40% of people leave their pets behind when they evacuate, and about half of them try to rescue their pets later." About one-third of these attempted "pet rescues" come during the hours of darkness, greatly increasing not only the risk to the owners but to those who might have to rescue them. "Animal ownership," he concludes, "may be the single most important cause of human evacuation failure." This also applies to ranchers who want to feed, check on, or rescue their stock. If the pets and livestock are not evacuated or rescued, emergency crews may well have to go back in and rescue their owners (or, as the case may be, to recover their remains).

Animal rescues also generate an extraordinary amount of publicity, both good and bad. The success or failure of high-profile animal rescue may have a long-term effect on an agency's image (and funding). It also falls under the general heading of "customer service" and maintaining good relations with the citizens who pay the bills.

Finally, it's the right and humane thing to do, consistent with the considerations we'll discuss in chapter 1.

Who rescues animals?

Generally speaking, there are two kinds of people who may be called upon to do flood and swiftwater rescues of animals. One is animal welfare and control personnel, who know a lot about animal behavior, but usually not much about moving water. The first chapters of this book, dealing with the characteristics of moving water, is intended for this group.

The other group is rescue personnel. These may have knowledge of swiftwater, but usually do not have much knowledge of handling animals, although in both cases this obviously varies with the individual. The later chapters of this book are intended for this group. Unlike a century ago, when most Americans lived on farms, most Americans today are urban dwellers who often have little idea of how to handle animals, especially large ones. There is also the "Babe" syndrome—movies and television shows that often give us the impression that animals think and act like humans. They do not!

Most of the animals you will be expected to rescue are domesticated animals; that is, they are used to being around humans. However, you will sometimes encounter "exotics."

4

Chapter One

Rescue philosophy and considerations

Mitigation:

It makes sense to try to mitigate the effect of disasters on both human and animal populations, before, during, and after the disaster. This reduces the danger to both and reduces the work load of emergency services personnel. Some effective mitigation measures are:

Evacuate pets along with people

Except in emergency situation where evacuations must be done in a hurry, in general it is a good idea to evacuate pets and owners together. This may seem a like an imposition at the time, but it greatly reduces the possibility of owner rescues later, and also increases the percentage of evacuees. A good rule of thumb is that if the situation is dangerous enough to require evacuation of people, the pets should come out, too.

John Davenport/San Antonio News Express

The most common reason given for owners not evacuating their pets with them was the owner's belief that they would not be gone long. Another common reason was simply poor owner attachment and ownership practices. Other reasons include not having a place to take the animals, not being able to catch them, and not having a carrier. (Heath 1999)

Evacuate animals with people whenever possible. Here a San Antonio firefighter helps a resident and his dog escape flood waters.

Public education and owner preparedness

As with many other areas, a good public education program will reduce problems later. Some suggestions are:

- Pet owners should be educated to realize that they, not EMS, are responsible for their pets.
- Owners should make up a pet emergency kit (see Appendix E) for each pet. A photo of each pet helps identify them.
- They should make prior arrangements to board animals outside the danger area, such as motels and relatives. Most disaster shelters cannot accept animals except service animals for the disabled.
- Small animal owners (cats, small dogs, etc.) should be encouraged to purchase a carrier for every cat.
- Encourage pet owners to use identification collars. Collared pets are easier to identify and are about 12 times more likely to be reunited with their owners. (Heath 1999)
- Consider using a two part tag system for pets and owners if they must be separated. Matching tag numbers is easier than locating pets and owners by description.

For farm and livestock owners:

- Livestock and horse owners should prepare for the possibility that they will have to evacuate their stock from flooded areas. They should scout evacuation routes to high ground and insure that adequate transportation is available.
- Make prior arrangements as to where evacuated stock will go.

Emergency Services

- EMS should expect and encourage people to evacuate with their pets.
- Set up a pet hotline for lost and separated pets.
- Set up a public education program for pet owners as described above, both before and during the disaster.
- Make reasonable accommodations for pet owners at shelters.

Rescue Philosophy

The general philosophy of swiftwater rescue is to rescue people and animals while exposing the rescuers to as little danger as possible under the circumstances. Prioritize the types of rescue by using the mnemonic RETHROG. This stands for:

- REach something like a pole or a stick to someone in the water.
- THrow a rope or ring buoy to them.
- ROw, paddle, or motor out on a boat to get them.
- Go to them for a hands-on swimming rescue.
- Helicopters are a high-risk option and should be considered a last resort.

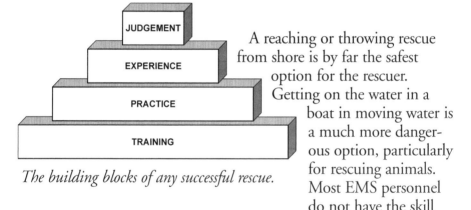

The building blocks of any successful rescue.

A reaching or throwing rescue from shore is by far the safest option for the rescuer. Getting on the water in a boat in moving water is a much more dangerous option, particularly for rescuing animals. Most EMS personnel do not have the skill and experience needed for boat handling in swift water. In-water swimming rescues are the most dangerous of all, and should be a last resort.

In general, choose the least dangerous, lowest tech, fastest rescue method. When considering rescue options, prioritize from low to high risk, low to high tech, fast to slow.

Remember: your own safety comes first. Rescue yourself, your team members second, and the victim, human or animal, last. In animal rescue situations there are two other considerations:

- Human rescues come before animal rescues.
- No unreasonable risk to humans when rescuing animals.

This last consideration pretty much rules out high risk rescue options for rescuing animals. Most animal rescues will be shore-based rescues of stranded animals done at the first responder level.

When dealing with animals RETHROG has to be modified.

Reach

Throw

Row

Go

Helo

The rescue sequence.

Talk/Lead:
        Most animals cannot understand verbal commands like "swim this way." However, they may be led to safety; or driven or induced to swim in certain directions.

Reach and throw:
        These rescue options are often limited, since most animals cannot grasp an extended pole or grasp a throw rope. There are some specialized tools like nets and snare poles that may work. These are described in chapter 3.

Row
Boat-based rescues are a high risk option with animals. Nevertheless this is a common solution and works fairly well *in calm water*. Rescuers must decide whether they need to get an animal in boat; lead it or get it to swim alongside; or attempt to herd it with a boat.

Go/Tow:
This option is usually too risky for humans, especially with larger animals. However, some in-water options like live bait may be okay if the risk is determined to be low. This leaves the hands free and provides a positive means of recovery.

Helo:
High risk option. Small animals must be restrained, caged and/or sedated before loading inside a helicopter. Large animals can sometimes be sling loaded underneath with commercial or improvised harnesses. However, *this is a job for experienced handlers only*. (See Appendix J)

Prepare by getting hands-on swiftwater training by a reputable trainer (see Appendix C).

Rescue options with animals:

Swimming animals:
- Getting a swimming animal out of the water can be difficult. Most animals, especially larger ones like cows and horses, require a short ramp or incline to get out of the water. Others, like cats, are good climbers.
- Most animals can swim, but may not swim in a safe direction. Some can be induced to swim towards safety or follow a boat. Others can be herded by boats or other means. It is usually safer to minimize contact by leading, driving, herding, or guiding large animals to safety. Animals can often be convinced to swim where you want them by using barriers, such as an inflated fire hose or pool floats in the water.
- Horses can sometimes be led with a halter behind a boat. However, the rescuers should be sure they can release if need be.

- Small animals (cats, dogs) can be scooped up with a pole net from shore or a boat. Scoop from the rear so as to keep the animal's head above water. Beware of breaking the net as the animal is lifted out of the water. You may have to leave a heavy animal in the water and pull or lead him over to shore.
- Use great caution when trying to get an animal in the boat, or when transporting animals in a boat. Adding a large animal to a boat in swift water invites trouble. Large animals may raise the center of gravity of the boat or upset the weight distribution. They will not know how to high side.

Stranded animals
- If the animal is no immediate danger, approach it as described below. Remember, a stranded animal may think its retreat is cut off and decide it must defend itself. It may also decide to retreat by swimming. Try to minimize your threat profile.
- Especially in a flash flood, where the water drops rapidly, consider placing food and water and leaving the animal in place. This should only be considered for short periods of time when doing so will not place the animal in danger from rising water.
- Try to channel animals where you want them to go. Use barriers (fences, traffic barriers, inflated fire hoses, etc.) to exclude them from some areas and direct their movements into others. Use positive reinforcement (e.g. food) to get them into areas where you do want them.

Personal Protective Equipment (PPE)

Swiftwater PPE
Personnel involved in flood or swiftwater rescue should have the proper PPE. Rescuers should *not* wear service uniforms, gun belts, or firefighting turnouts. Instead wear PPE appropriate for the situation.
- Use a **PERSONAL FLOTATION DEVICE** (PFD) appropriate for swiftwater. This means a USCG Type III or V PFD (no horse collars!) with 15-25 lbs/12-18kg designed for whitewater or swiftwater use. Always wear a PFD when within 10'/3m of the water. Attach a knife and a whistle to your PFD.
- A water rescue **helmet**.
- **Thermal protection** in the form of a wet or dry suit. A dry suit provides better protection from contaminated water but may cause overheating. Do not wear cotton clothing, which feels cold and clammy when wet. Instead wear synthetic insulating clothing like pile or natural insulators like wool under a waterproof nylon shell.
- **Foot protection**. You'll want a hard sole neoprene bootie or the equivalent to protect your feet from sharp rocks and debris.
- **Hand protection** is always a good idea when doing animal rescue. It protects you from bites and scratches and keeps your skin away from contaminated fur, saliva, feces, etc.

  However, the best protection for any rescuer is **knowledge** of moving water and hands-on instruction by a competent teacher.

Firefighting PPE
Do not wear firefighting turnouts, service belts and uniforms, or the like in the water! They will quickly become soaked with water and impede swimming. However, while firefighting turnouts are dangerous in the water, they may be useful for animal capture and during decon. The heavy coat and gloves offer considerable physical protection from claws and teeth.

Avoid risky behavior, such as:

- Tying yourself to a rope. While tethering yourself with a rope may seem like a good idea, it is not! A tethered swimmer is often forced under water and cannot either release the rope or be hauled back to shore because of the pressure of the water.
- Jumping in the water to rescue an animal without proper preparation and backup.
- Tying yourself to or swimming with a large animal like a horse or cow. If you do find yourself in the water with a large animal, stay on the upstream side!

Do not tie yourself to a rope when entering moving water! You may be pulled underwater and be unable to release it.

Self Rescue

Any flood or swiftwater rescuer must be prepared to rescue himself if he ends up in the water. For moving water this means:

- Face downstream.
- Keep your feet up. Your toes should be just breaking the surface. Don't try to stand up in the river! To do so may lead to foot entrapment.
- Assess the situation. Identify hazards such as strainers, hydraulics and the like, and swim away from them with a backstroke. Push off rocks with your feet.
- Look for an eddy or clear spot on the bank to land. Swim that way. If the water is deep, roll over on your stomach and swim to shore with a crawl stroke.
- Don't try to stand up until the you are in an eddy near shore and the water is ankle deep or shallower (safe eddy rule).

Site organization

Any swiftwater rescue site needs to be organized. All sites at a minimum need:

- **Upstream spotter.** One person should stay upstream of the site to stop river traffic and to warn rescuers of floating debris.
- **Downstream safety.** Establish downstream safety with boats, rescuers with throw bags, or both. No one should be allowed to get downstream of the last safety!
- **Incident command.** Some form of incident command system needs to be set up, and a system of personnel accountability.

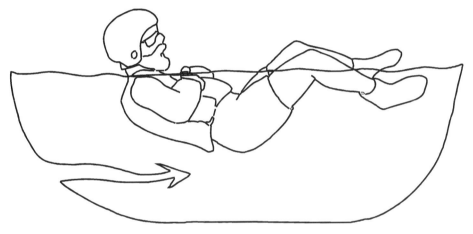

The safe swimming position: facing downstream with the feet up. Fend off rocks with your feet, and do not try to stand up until you reach a safe eddy. If the water is deep, roll over and swim with a crawl stroke.

Hydrology and hazards

River orientation

All rivers are described the same way. There are four directions: *river right* and *river left* are the right and left banks of the river looking downstream. The other two directions are *upstream* and *downstream*. This standard system of reference allows us to reduce confusion when describing the location of an incident or victim.

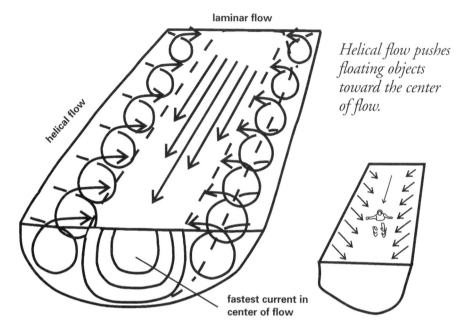

Helical flow pushes floating objects toward the center of flow.

River cross section. Helical flow corkscrews along the bank. Laminar flow moves down the center, the fastest in the middle.

Hydrology

Moving water has three characteristics: it is **powerful**; it is **relentless**; and it is **predictable** to the experienced eye. How powerful? A 6mph/9.6km/sec current pushes on a submerged human body with 134lbf/596N. This force increases in an exponential rather than a linear fashion. If the current velocity is doubled to 12mph/19.3km/hr the amount of force *quadruples* (to 538lbf/2.4kN)! If you are pushed against something in the river it will be extremely difficult to escape.

Water Force

Current velocity mph/kmh	On legs lbf/N	On body lbf/N	On swamped boat lbf/N
3/4.8	16/71.1	33.6/149.5	168/747.3
6/9.7	67.2/299	134/596.1	672/2989
9/14.5	151/671.7	302/1343.4	1512/6725.7
12/19.3	269/1196.6	538/2393	2688/11956.8

Water pushes against anything in its path, like vehicles. Two feet (.6m) of moving water will float most vehicles. On a hard surface, however, one foot (.3m) of water moving at 6mph (10 km/hr) will move most cars. Because of this vehicle searches must be conducted with caution, and citizens and rescuers kept away from low water crossings, ditches, and other places where moving water may catch them.

River features

All moving water works the same way—it's just a matter of scale. The main flow of the river is a **laminar flow**: similar to a series of sheets of water stacked above one another. The fastest flow is in the center just below the surface, the slowest on the bottom. The water on the sides of the river flows in a corkscrewing motion called **helical flow.** Helical flow tends to push objects toward the center of the river. If the river flows around a bend the momentum of the river pushes the main current against the outside of the bend, increasing erosion there while depositing sediment on the inside of the bend.

Obstacles in the river like boulders cause water to pile up in front of them in a pillow. Eddies form behind them. Water in the eddies flows back upstream. Water flowing between two obstacles forms a downstream **V** or tongue. This indicates the clearest path between the obstacles and the deepest water. There are usually waves at the bottom of the tongue as the water gives up its energy. Underwater obstacles are frequently marked by an upstream **V**.

Hazards

Holes and hydraulics: when water begins to flow over obstacles it forms a breaking wave called a hole. This is capable of upsetting boats but generally will not hold a floating object for any length of time. Far more dangerous is the hydraulic, which is a recirculating current behind the obstacle. A hydraulic will hold floating objects for extended periods of time, and can be very difficult to escape from. The worst hydraulics form behind low-head dams or weirs.

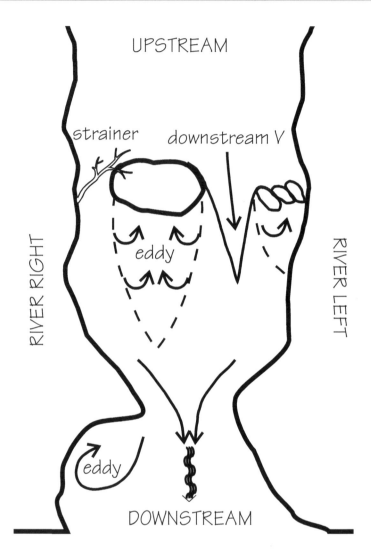

River directions: upstream, downstream, river right and left. River left and right are always defined when looking downstream. Solid obstacles create eddies. A downstream V or tongue forms where the water flows between obstacles. Obstacles like tree branches that allow water to flow through them create strainers.

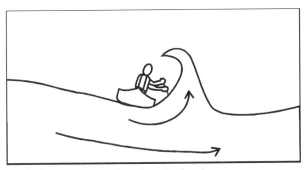

A hole is a wave that breaks back upstream.

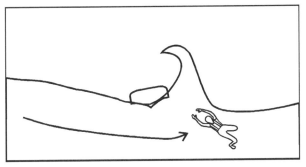

It is a surface phenomenon that will not hold a swimmer.

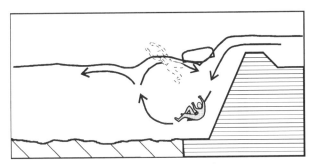

A hydraulic is a full depth recirculating current that may keep an object for an extended period.

Hydraulics are often found at the base of low-head dams but also occur naturally.

Strainers: A strainer is any object in the current that will allow water to flow thorough it but not solid objects (like people). Some examples are trees and fences. Strainers are extremely dangerous since a person can be pushed up against them by the force of the current and be unable to escape. Boulder and debris piles can also act as strainers.

Man-made debris: Old river structures like abandoned dams, mills, and bridges can leave structural debris like reinforcing rods in the river. Rivers may also have been used as dumps and have potential hazards like old autos, appliances, and the like.

Undercuts, foot & body entrapment: Many natural rock features on the river may be undercut. If a boat or person is forced into this undercut they will probably be held there by the force of the current and drown. Undercuts can often be identified by the lack of a pillow on the upstream side of the rock.

If a swimmer's foot or other extremity becomes wedged in a crack or crevice in the river bed, the force of the water will push them down and keep them from escaping. Many people drown this way. It is why swimmers should never try to stand up in moving water.

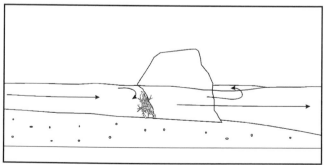

Do not stand up in moving water! If your foot gets lodged in the river bed the force of the current will prevent you from escaping.

Undercut rocks are especially dangerous. A boat or person may be pushed underneath and held there.

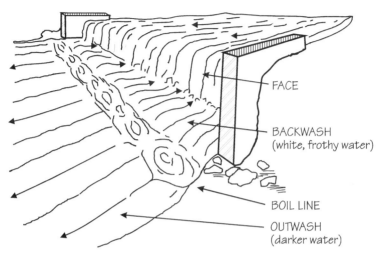

A typical low-head dam.

Cold water: Still water pulls heat from the body about twenty-five times as fast as air; moving water about 250 times as fast. Hypothermia—the uncontrolled lowering of body temperature—can cause debility and eventually death. Even mild immersion hypothermia can lead to loss of function of the extremities and interfere with the ability to self-rescue. This is especially true in situations like foot entrapment where a victim is fixed in position and the current is flowing past him. Immersion in cold water may also cause a gasping reflex that may cause swimmers to aspirate water in big waves.

HAZMAT considerations: Rescuers must also protect themselves from what is in the water. It is not unusual for flooded water treatment plants to release large amounts of untreated sewage; water flowing through farms may contain pesticides or other agricultural chemicals; and water flowing through urban areas can pick up large amounts of toxic chemicals of all kinds.

Swiftwater rescue equipment

Besides a rescuer's PPE, the most common piece of rescue equipment is the throw bag, a nylon fabric bag with 25-75' (7.6-21m) of rope, usually 3/8" (9.5mm) stuffed inside. This allows a rescuer to make throwing rescues fairly close to shore.

Another need is communications. Recent advances in technology make this easier with inexpensive handheld radios and cellular phones.

Rescuers will often use boats for flood and swiftwater rescue. Boat handling and selection is beyond the scope of this book, but suffice it to say that boats must be selected with swiftwater operation in mind, and that rescue boat crews need to have swiftwater or whitewater-specific training before putting in on moving water.

Chapter Two

Communication: animal behavior

Todd Feebeck/Kansas City Star

Nine-year-old Crystal Reynolds plays with her hamster, Rowdy, the family's sole pet survivor of the 1998 Kansas City flood. "Pocket pets" like hamsters, mice, gerbils, and the like, are becoming increasingly popular.

Introduction

The ability of humans to communicate with animals varies widely. Animals can't understand verbal directions in human languages, except for perhaps a few simple words like "outside." Even human gestures that we interpret as friendly may be interpreted by an animal as threatening, especially during periods of stress.

This leads to a basic rule of animal behavior: *if an animal is threatened with harm, or what it perceives as harmful, it will defend itself as best it can.* The weapons vary widely but the reaction can be swift, violent, and occasionally deadly. In short—you can get hurt if you're not careful.

It follows, then, that the best way to deal with an animal is to convince it that you mean it no harm. This may be difficult if the animal is already in a life-threatening situation, such as in a flood. Since logical discourse with an animal is not an option (unless perhaps you have Dr. Doolittle along), you can deal with them by either physically restraining them or by convincing them to do what you want them to.

For large, heavy, powerful animals like horses the preferred method is to get them to cooperate. For small, skittish animals like cats, restraint is the best option.

As a rescuer, you need to understand enough about the animal's instincts, physical characteristics, and psychological makeup to make an intelligent decision about what your options are.

Animal behavior is driven far more by instinct that is that of humans. In disasters animals follow their instincts more than what we would consider reason. Like humans, they may panic and exhibit non-purposeful behavior. For the rescuer, it is important to know how different animals react. Sometimes, animals are not aware that they need to be rescued. Dogs, for example, will often continue to defend their territory against rescuers. Domestic animals act differently when their owners are not around.

Most animals will retreat from danger; however, when the "attacker" moves within a certain critical distance, they will launch a pre-emptive attack. Remember: a stranded animal often cannot retreat!

Body language is much more important to animals than words. Much of animal communication is done by species-specific postures, gestures and actions. These may communicate such varied themes as sexual interest, dominance, or threat display. When approaching an animal remember:

• **Move slowly**. Quick, decisive movements are usually interpreted as an attack. The profile of the person advancing also is important. Many animals use a "threat display:" that is, they make themselves look larger and more threatening than they actually are to ward off attackers or cow rivals. Thus a cat arches his back and makes his hair stand up, a dog's hair stands up around his neck and back. This is a warning: push me and I'll attack. So it's usually a good idea to lower your profile when approaching a small animal to make yourself look less threatening. You can squat or approach sideways to make yourself look smaller.

• **Avoid eye contact** with any animal, wild or domestic, since this is usually interpreted as an invitation to a confrontation. Especially true of dogs, since this is a way of establishing dominance. Look away from the animal or toward the ground.

• **Speak softly.** Shouting at an animal generally gets a negative response, since harsh sounds are generally associated with an attack.

In general, keep your voice low and pleasant, using a soothing, non-threatening tone. How you say it is much more important than what you say. However, some domestic animals, particularly dogs and horses, can often be controlled with familiar commands like "sit."

Small animals

Firefighter Stan Kinnard smiles after rescuing three puppies from the 1997 floods in Cincinnati, OH.

Glenn/Hartong/Cincinnati Enquirer

Dogs

Attack profile: bites.
- Dogs are pack animals. They like to be with other dogs and will chase and attack something small that runs away or screams i.e. children, other dogs.

- Many dogs will defend their territory even when it puts them in danger. There have been numerous cases of guard dogs "protecting" burning houses from firefighters. Dogs bred for guarding or fighting (Chows, Mastiffs, Pit Bulls) are the most dangerous, but do not assume any dog is "safe" until he is under positive control.
- Most dogs signal an attack by barking or by a bluff charge, but some do not. Beware the dog who attacks without barking or showing any of the body language covered below.
- The "kill zone" is about halfway between the front door and your car. It is a good idea to announce your arrival.
- Keep something like an EMS bag or pack between you and a dog you aren't sure of. If he attacks give it to him to bite. Leave yourself an escape route.

Approach: lower your profile; avoid eye contact; talk in a low, soothing voice. Approach slowly.

Dog language
- Head up, teeth bared, hair up on back and neck: I'm ready to attack.
- Head down, tail between legs: I submit—you're the boss. However, even cowering dogs may bite out of simple fear.
- Front legs stretched out, back curved down: Let's play.
- Head up, tail wagging, barking: I'm not sure who you are and I think my boss ought to know you're here (but I still might bite you).

Handling a dog
- Control the head—a dog attacks with his teeth. Hold large dogs on the side and back of the head to control it.
- To lift a dog, use one hand to control the head, then support the dog's weight by lifting from behind his rear legs or, for small dogs, under the abdomen.
- Use a muzzle. This disarms the dog's primary weapon—his teeth. TIP: An improvised muzzle can be made from surgical tubing or a tourniquet (this will not work on very blunt-

nosed dogs). WARNING: Do not muzzle a panting dog!
Dogs do not sweat. They vent excess heat by panting.
A muzzled dog may die very quickly from overheating.

- Try to work from a distance: use nooses, catchpoles, and pole nets to hold the dog so that others can move around behind it to immobilize its head to get a muzzle on (see chapter 3).
- Take a leash with you. Many dogs respond positively to being leashed.
- Small dogs can be controlled by "scruffing" like cats.
- Transfer the dog into a pen or enclosure as soon as possible.

One way to control a dog. Trina Hudson holds the head in the crook of her arm, with her hand on the back of the dog's head. The other arm controls the dog's hind quarters. Note the heavy gloves.

Small dogs can be "scruffed." Grasp the loose skin behind the dog's head and pull tight to control the head. Support the dog's weight with the other hand.

Cats

A rescuer climbs a ladder to rescue a cat trapped by flood waters in Cincinnati, OH.

Glenn Hartong/Cincinnati Enquirer

Attack profile: scratches, then bites.
- Cat bites and scratches are prone to infection.
- House cats don't attack unless cornered, but see large cats section below.
- Flattened ears are a sign of imminent attack.

Approach: lower profile, avoid eye contact, talk in a low, soothing voice. Approach slowly. Wear gloves and forearm protection!

Handling a cat

- TIP: A large towel or blanket often makes an effective tool for capturing a cat. Throw it over the cat and quickly wrap it up.
- Control a cat by "scruffing" it. Grasp it by the loose skin on the back of the neck and shoulders and pull tight. This controls the head and keeps the cat from biting you, as well as keeping his front claws away. Then grab the cat's back legs with your other hand. This immobilizes the cat and makes it impossible for him to attack you.
- Use a sack or large bag for temporary holding or transport. Put the cat in the bag butt-first and quickly secure the top. Make sure it has adequate ventilation. Don't use a pillow case—a cat will shred it in short order and escape.
- Use a cage or carrier for long-term holding or transporting a cat.

Scruff a cat to keep it from biting or scratching you. Grab the loose skin behind the neck to control the head and front legs, and use the other hand to hold the back legs.

Large Animals

Randy Pench/Sacramento Bee

Large animals like horses present different problems for rescuers. Here a volunteer tries to round up a horse stranded during the January 1997 floods in Central California.

Horses

Attack profile: Runs away if possible, but will kick, strike with its hooves and bite if cornered or threatened.

Safety considerations
- Horses can kill. A horse is a large, powerful animal that can cause severe injury in a confined space like a stall, even if it means you no harm. Be careful!
- Beware of being kicked. The danger zone for kicking is 3-10' (1-3m) from the horses hind quarters. Either stay right next to the animal or move a safe (15-20', 5-7m) distance away. Watch the back legs—they will reach further than you think.

Body language
- If the horse's eyes widen, his muscles noticeably tense up, and he blows out through his nostrils, he is getting agitated. Exercise caution.
- Flattened ears are a sigh of an imminent attack.

Approach
- Most horses are gentle and naturally curious. They are used to being led and to being around people (this obviously does not apply to wild horses). Some are skittish, however, and you need to reassure the horse that you mean it no harm.
- Announce your presence by whistling or talking gently. Don't shout. Use a low, calming voice when talking. Don't face the horse directly.
- Use bait to exploit a horse's natural curiosity. Rattle pebbles in a can, crinkle paper in your pocket, or offer food.
- Horses have eyes on the sides of their heads, which gives them a wide field of vision to see predators. However, unlike humans, they do not see very well straight ahead. Try to approach a horse from the front quarter rather than from straight ahead to avoid startling it.
- Use slow, deliberate movements around horses, who some times spook easily. Don't wave or jump.
- Do not use the lights or sirens on emergency vehicles around horses.

Handling
- Horses are herd animals. They like to be with other horses and to follow an established leader. You can sometimes use this instinct to your advantage. If you can lead one horse where you want it to go, especially a dominant one, you can often get the others to follow.
- If possible, try to use the horse's owner, or someone experienced in handling horses, to help with the rescue. Handling horses in a disaster requires experience.
- The best place to stand is just behind the horse's left shoulder. Stroke or scratch the horse's shoulder and talk to him in a soothing voice. Be patient and win his confidence.

- Put on a halter. This gives you a way to control the horse's head. If you can do this you will control the rest of him. Walk next to the horse's left shoulder about an arm's length away.
- Lead the horse with a halter if possible. If you can't lead the horse, you may be able to herd it where you want it to go. Don't try to improvise a halter unless you know what you're doing. You can blindfold an agitated horse to calm it.
- Don't tie yourself to a horse, especially in the water. Don't tie anything to a horse unless you know what you're doing or have been directed to do so by an experienced horse handler. You can injure or kill the horse and yourself.
- Don't get into the water with a horse or try to ride a horse through water, especially moving water.
- Most boats are not suitable for carrying horses. Horses are tall and raise the center of gravity enough to make almost any boat unstable, not to mention that the animal's reactions may be unpredictable.

Erhardt Krause/Sacramento Bee

A rescuer leads a horse to safety during the 1997 California floods. The cattle have chosen the high ground.

Cows

Cattle are herd animals who like to stay together. Unlike horses, they are not used to being handled individually, but rather herded as a group.

Attack profile: Butts with its head. They can also kick with their hind legs.

Safety considerations
- Generally, cattle are less dangerous than horses (this does not apply to bulls).
- Some breeds have large horns that can cause serious injury.
- Some breeds weigh well over a thousand pounds are can cause serious injury just by their size, especially in confined areas like stalls.

Body language
- Stands its ground and lowers its head: attack likely.
- Turns head and moves away: submission.

Approach
- Approach slowly and deliberately. Talk in a slow, low, soothing tone.
- Keep a safe distance away.
- Allow yourself an escape route.

Handling
- Herd cattle where you want them to go rather than trying to capture them. Keep them together and lead or drive them into a pen or enclosure.
- Herd slowly. Don't wave your arms and shout.

Pigs

Attack profile: Charges and bites.

Safety considerations
- Farm pigs are domesticated but not used to being handled.
- A recent trend has been the keeping of pet pigs such as the Vietnamese Pot-Bellied at home. These pigs are more used to people and to being handled. However, they set up an bloody racket when picked up.
- Wild pigs have large tusks that can cause serious injury.
- Pigs have strong jaws and can cause serious wounds. Their bites are "dirty" and can easily become infected.
- Use adequate safety precautions when entering an enclosure with a large pig. Leave yourself an escape route.
- Approach sows with litters with caution.

Handling
- Pigs are intelligent, stubborn and unpredictable. They are also strong and can move quickly. Even a small pig can be difficult to physically capture.
- Pigs have a limited cooling ability and overheat quickly. They do not handle stress well.
- Pigs are difficult to herd and often seem to do exactly the opposite of what you want them to do. They can also exhibit a "mob" reaction under stress; that is, if one pig squeals, the rest may attack.
- Best to deal with pigs separately rather than in a group. Use a large object like a board, stretcher or litter, to direct the pig(s) into a pen, cage, or enclosure. Pigs can be guided (sometimes) by tapping them on their sides or heads with a stick.
- Use food to induce the pig to go where you want him to go.

Sheep

Sheep are herd animals with a strong instinct to stay together. If separated from the flock sheep may panic and injure themselves.

Attack profile: Rams butt with their heads. Otherwise sheep don't kick or bite and are relatively easy to handle.

Body language: Lowered head is a sign of imminent attack.

Safety considerations
- Relatively low chance of serious injury.
- Sheep overheat easily.

Handling
- Sheep are best handled by experienced shepherds and sheep dogs.
- Herd or guide the flock with boards, panels, litters, etc.
- Approach slowly, reduce threat posture, and speak softly. Don't yell or wave.
- Don't grab a sheep by the wool if you need to handle it. This can damage the wool and injure the sheep. If you need to handle a single sheep, place one hand on the animal's chin or chest to stop it, then place the other hand on the animal's rear just under the tail (dock). Move the sheep where you want it to go.
- Because of sheep's tendency to panic if separated from the flock, it is usually better to capture a single sheep directly from the flock rather than cutting it out.

Goats

Goats are herd animals and like to stay together. They are more intelligent than sheep and can be pesky critters to deal with.

Attack profile: Males butt with their heads. Attacks are more likely than with sheep.

Body language
- Lowered head means attack imminent.
- Goats will put on a threat display by vocalizing and stamping their feet, but will not attack when captured.

Safety considerations
- Little danger of serious injury to handlers.
- Goats can be easily injured by rough handling. Their bones are delicate and easily broken. They are prone to stress when captured and restrained.

Approach: Approach slowly, minimize threat profile, and speak softly.

Handling
- Goats are quite agile, are good jumpers, and can often quickly figure out how to escape restraint (opening gates, chewing ropes, etc.).
- Capture and guide like a sheep: one hand in front of chest and the other beneath the tail.
- You can grab a goat's horns to capture it, but they don't like to be led this way.
- Herd goats by directing them into a pen or enclosure.

Exotics

In some areas (e.g. south Florida), many people keep exotic pets, so you never know what you will encounter. In a recent flood in Mississippi, several hundred alligators floated out of a alligator farm during high water. These animals are not "domesticated" in the normal sense of the word.

Ostrich, Emu, etc.

These large, flightless birds have been kept in recent years as "stock."

Attack profile: Prefers to run, but if cornered will kick with feet.

General attack sequence is
- Threat display: puffs up, stands erect
- Bluff attack
- Real attack

Safety Considerations
- Do not wear anything shiny (watches, glasses, jewelry), because like many birds they will peck at it.
- Their kick is extremely powerful and is capable of severely injuring or even killing an adult.
- These birds can kick straight forward only. Avoid attack by moving laterally back and forth in front of the bird so that he can't "square" on you. He can't kick at an angle.

Handling
- These birds are not terribly intelligent and are relatively easy to outsmart.
- An umbrella is a good tool. Open it to intimidate the birds by making yourself look larger.
- Use the crook of the umbrella or a similar tool to pull the bird's head down. He can't kick with his head down.
- To subdue, get the bird's head down and under control. Then put something opaque over it, like a hood or jacket. This will calm the bird. Leave the hood on when moving or transporting the bird.
- To move the bird, put one person on each side to control it.

Iguanas
Often kept as pets in tropical regions.

Attack profile: Prefers to run, but if cornered will attack by biting and clawing. The Iguana also has a long, sharp, tail that it uses like a whip. It can cut you.

Body language: Opens mouth and hisses when threatened or annoyed.

Safety considerations
- When handling an Iguana be sure to keep positive control of its head, feet and tail.
- Wear turnouts, gloves, or other protective clothing.

Handling
- Iguanas are good swimmers and good climbers. They generally try to escape by climbing. They are afraid of dogs.
- A good way to catch them is to run them into a high perch, then put a noose over their head.

Large cats (cougars, ocelots, etc.)
Some people keep large cats like Ocelots and cougars for pets.

Attack profile
Bites, claws. Larger cats can inflict serious injury. Unlike smaller cats, they may stand their ground on their own territory or even stalk humans.

Safety considerations
- Minimum distance for attack/retreat is about 25'/7.6m.
- Big cats view size changes differently than most animals mentioned so far. They are programmed to stalk and attack smaller animals. Therefore you do not want to reduce your profile suddenly, as by kneeling, since this may encourage an attack. Keep small animals and children away, and do not approach by yourself.

- Don't make sudden moves or stalk them.
- Don't corner them if possible.
- Large objects that appear solid (blue tarp, cardboard, etc.) can be used to herd the cat where you want him to go.

Body language: Crouched, ears laid back means unpredictable behavior.

Handling: Making a twirring sound and slowly blinking eyes has a calming effect.

Llamas and Alpacas

These have become popular in recent years as pack animals. They are herd animals; the Alpaca more so than the Llama and therefore easier to control.

Attack profile: Not particularly dangerous, but both species have "fighting teeth" that can cause injury.

Safety considerations: Beware of "berserk male syndrome:" a male who sees humans as competing males and will attack them.

Handling
- Llamas and Alpacas often lie down when in danger. This can be frustrating when you are trying to rescue them.
- Both Llamas and Alpacas have a nasty habit of spitting when annoyed. Those animals who have close human contact have often been trained not to spit.
- These animals dislike dark places. They will resist being loaded into an enclosed trailer.
- If they have a halter on, use it to lead the animal. Some owners leave the halters on all the time.
- They do not show pain in an obvious way. This can make it difficult to assess injuries.

Snakes

Snakes are often kept as pets, and may escape during floods. This can include very large ones like boa constrictors, and extremely poisonous ones. Unless you are very sure what you are dealing with it is usually better to let a herp expert do it. If you suspect non-native species are involved, do not assume you can identify which ones are dangerous and which ones are not.

Attack profile
- Poisonous snakes strike with their fangs.
- Constrictors wrap around their prey and suffocate them. Extremely large constrictors are dangerous to humans.

Safety considerations
- Beware of snakes during floods! Rising water runs snakes out of their holes and you have to be very careful where you step. They may end up on islands and on floating debris with human or other animal victims.
- Snakes generally make threat displays and warn before they strike.
- Many snake bites happen when someone inadvertently steps on a snake. If conditions permit wear heavy boots in snake-infested areas.

Handling
- Smaller snakes can be safely captured using a piece of PVC pipe with a bag on the end. The snake is looking for a small, dark place to hide in. It will enter pipe and can then be cinched down in the bag.
- If you must handle a snake, control the head. Even a non-poisonous snake can give you a painful bite.

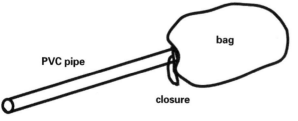

A snake catcher. A bag with a draw closure is attached to a length of PVC pipe. The snake crawls down the pipe and into the bag, which is then secured.

Wolves, coyotes, and wolf-dog hybrids

Wolf-dog hybrids have become fairly common as pets and may be encountered even in urban areas. Most attacks are by hybrids, whose behavior tends to be unpredictable. No rules apply to coyotes. Like other canines these are pack animals whose behavior is similar to other dogs.

Identification: large canine teeth, black spot on tail, short rounded ears with furry insides; dense shoulder ruff; coarse guard hairs on coat, long tail that does not curl; slanted eyes.

Attack profile: bites

Approach
- Don't point.
- Avoid staring.
- Keep your body profile low and small to reduce perceived threat.
- Keep menstruating females away.

Handling
- In general, handled like other canines. Expect the worst and exert positive control.
- A muzzle is *always* a good idea.

Chapter Three

Handling and transport of animals

Hazards

Best defense for chemical contamination or disease is normal protective measures against blood-borne pathogens: gloves, splash protection, eye and face protection, etc. It is a good idea to minimize contact with any animal whose medical history you are unsure of, or who you have just pulled from the water. Decontaminate both yourself and the animal after rescue, and make sure your immunizations are up to date.

Disease

In addition to the obvious dangers of being, bitten, trampled, gored and scratched, there is also the possibility of catching a nasty disease from the animals that you are handling. Some animal diseases are zoonotic that is, they can be transmitted from animals to humans. Some of the most common (but by no means all) are:

Rabies

- Viral disease causing serious brain damage and death if untreated. Transmitted via the animal's saliva by bites, scratches, or any breaks in the skin.
- Any warm-blooded animal, including humans, can be infected. Any animal bite should be considered a potential infection, but this is especially true of wild animals like raccoons, bats, skunks, foxes, etc. If possible, bring in the suspected animal (or its head) for examination or quarantine.
- If bitten, wash wound site immediately with soap and water, then consult with a physician or your medical control as soon as possible.
- Symptoms begin 2-8 weeks after exposure. They include malaise, headache, fever, and anxiety. Rabies may eventually cause numbness, paralysis, coma, and death.
- Treatment must start early to be effective. Rabies Immune Globulin (RIG) can be given immediately, followed by a series of shots.
- Report all animal bites, even minor ones, to your medical control.

Cat Scratch Fever

- Rickettsial infection caused by cat scratches or bites. The cat may show no symptoms.
- Wound will be red and sore, changing to an open sore that eventually dries up.
- Not fatal, but may cause fatigue, fever, and swollen lymph nodes. Symptoms begin 3-14 days after exposure. Doctor's care may be needed in severe cases.
- Clean all scratches well and monitor for infection.

Brucellosis (undulant fever)

- Affects cattle and related species, causing spontaneous abortions. However, it can be transmitted to humans.
- Bacterial disease transmitted by blood, feces, tissue or urine of an infected animal. Not transmitted person-to-person.
- Enters body through cuts or mucous membranes.
- Symptoms include fever, chills, weight loss, body and joint aches beginning 1-2 months after exposure. Early treatment with antibiotics effective.
- Prophylaxis: clean wounds, wear protective clothing and gloves when handling livestock.

Bubonic Plague

- Bacterial infection transmitted from rodents to humans via fleas. Can also be transmitted by bites or scratches. Pneumonic variety is transmitted by airborne droplets coughed by humans or animals, causing an infection in the lungs.
- Rare, found mostly in southwestern U.S.
- Causes swelling of lymph nodes, chills, weakness, nausea and fatigue one to seven days after flea bite.
- High mortality rate (50% untreated), but can be effectively treated with antibiotics.
- Use caution when handling small mammals, especially dead ones or any who appear to be sick.

Hantavirus

- Viral upper respiratory disease transmitted by rodent droppings. Common in the Americas.
- Fatality rate of over 50% even if treated.
- High risk factor where large rodent population exists—use protection if searching old buildings. Contracted by breathing infected dust in enclosed spaces.
- Avoid stirring up dust. Open doors and windows; wet surfaces with disinfectant or 10% bleach solution to clean them rather than using a broom or vacuum.
- Avoid contact with rodents or droppings; disinfect and double bag them for disposal by burning or burying.
- Wear a HEPA respirator mask, gloves, coveralls, and rubber boots. Decontaminate when finished.

Leptospirosis

- Water-borne disease spread by urine. Often associated with livestock areas.
- Rain washes bacteria into streams and rivers, where it may survive for up to six months. May also be contracted from contact with infected soil.
- Several related bacteria infect both humans and various species of animals (swine, livestock, dogs, cats, sheep, rats, and many others). Cross-infections very likely.
- Debilitating (diarrhea, fever, and cramping) and hard to get rid of. May cause kidney failure if left untreated. Can be treated with antibiotics.
- Use general protection against waterborne diseases and for handling animals.

Giardia

- Intestinal disorder caused by waterborne micro organism, *Giardia lamblia*, that attaches to the small intestine.
- Spread by fecal contamination.
- Not fatal, but causes diarrhea, bloating, gas, and cramping.
- Hard to identify and get rid of. Symptoms may begin weeks after exposure.

- Use general protection against waterborne diseases. Purify all water.

Rocky Mountain Spotted Fever
- Tick-borne infection caused by rickettsia.
- Symptoms include fever, loss of appetite, headache, muscle pain, nausea, and skin rash.
- Laboratory tests needed to confirm; effective treatment with antibiotics if diagnosed early.
- Use normal measures (long pants, etc.) to reduce exposure to ticks. Remove any ticks as soon as possible—the longer the tick stays attached (<24 hours) the greater the likelihood of infection.
- Seek medical attention immediately if symptoms develop.

Lyme Disease
- Bacterial infection transmitted by the bite of certain species of tick. Affects humans and animals.
- Usually starts as a skin rash near the bite site. If untreated may affect nerve, joint, or heart tissue.
- Can be effectively treated with antibiotics if detected early.
- Use normal measures (long pants, etc.) to reduce exposure to ticks. Remove any ticks as soon as possible—the longer the tick stays attached (<24 hours) the greater the likelihood of infection.
- If bitten, remove tick gently, avoid pulling off head if possible. Swab the wound site with antiseptic or wash with soap and water. Monitor the wound site for skin rash.
- Save tick in alcohol for identification, and report bite to medical control.

Contamination
- Floods are, by definition, HAZMAT incidents. Assume that all the animals you are rescuing are contaminated and that they will contaminate you. Many animals have fur or hair that may become saturated with contaminants, and these will be transferred to you when you handle them.

- Wear normal medical protection: gloves, mask, and protective clothing when handling animals during or after rescue.
- Set up immediate post-rescue decontamination for animals as well as humans. Do this before the animals are transferred to permanent holding facilities.
- Wear protective clothing when on or near the water, as conditions permit. Protective clothing that excludes water (dry suits) protects better than those that do not (wet suits). Attempt to minimize animal contact to unprotected areas of your body (e.g. face and hands).
- Many animals, like dogs, instinctively shake themselves after getting wet and may spread contamination this way.
- Don't forget to decon equipment, too: trailers, cages, nets, poles, clothing, PPE, etc.
- Decontaminate personnel often. Track them throughout the event. Where were they today?

Basic animal first aid

Because of their unfamiliarity with veterinary medicine and lack of specialized medical equipment, rescuers are limited in their abilities to give first aid to animals.

Safety considerations
- Rescuers should not put themselves at risk attempting to rescue or assist an injured animal. Many animals, especially larger ones, are capable of seriously injuring or killing a rescue worker.
- When approaching a "downed" large animal, stay clear of the animal's legs, even if it appears to be unresponsive. Instead, approach from the animal's back. Announce your approach to avoid startling it.
- Small animals are more likely to bite or scratch if they are injured. Wear heavy gloves when handling them and observe handling precautions already discussed (i.e. "scruffing").

Initial actions

Rescuers should locate, identify, and triage animals in the risk zone, and get this information back to veterinary professionals. Based on the circumstances, a decision will have to be made whether to attempt to evacuate the animal to a veterinary facility or to treat (or possibly euthanize) the animal in place.

LOCATE: injured animals

IDENTIFY: species, physical description (color, height, weight etc.; see Appendix F), nature and severity of injuries.

MARK: location of animal

ASSESS: the animal's injuries and indicate whether injuries are minor, moderate, or severe.

EVACUATE: if the situation and the nature of the animal's injuries permit.

COMMUNICATE: the location and nature of the animal's injuries to veterinary professionals if evacuation is not possible.

Treatment

- Before beginning treatment insure that you are not placing yourself in danger i.e. either that the animal is docile and/or that it is restrained.
- Check for vital signs: temperature, heart rate, and respiration (see table). Animal temperatures must be taken rectally, something most will not be disposed to have done without restraint.
- An excellent indication of the status of many animals is Capillary Refill Time (CRT). Check by pressing a finger against the animal's gums until the membrane blanches, then note the time that it takes for it to return to normal color. For most animals this will be 1-2 seconds.

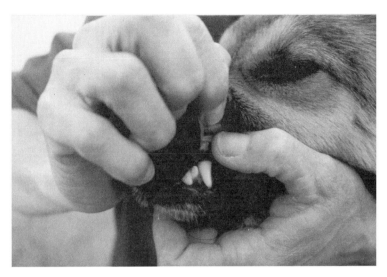

Check Capillary Refill Time by pressing in on the animal's gum, then releasing pressure and seeing how long it takes to return to normal color.

Animal vital signs

Normal	Rectal temperature	Heart rate	Respiration
Dog	101	70-130/min	30
Cat	101	70-130	30
Horse	100.5	30-50	12/min
Cattle	101.5	60-70	30
Sheep	103	60-120	20
Goat	102	70-100	20
Pig	102	60-80	20

Cuts, lacerations, and open bleeding wounds:
Handled more or less the same way as on humans: direct pressure until the bleeding stops, followed by bandaging. For large wounds on large animals, use duct tape to hold the dressing in place.

Impaled objects
Leave in place if possible. If the object projects you may need to trim it down closer to the body.

Broken limbs
These are best left to veterinarians. If the animal is docile you can splint it according to normal practice. Large animals with broken limbs are often destroyed, but this is a decision for a veterinarian.

Eye injuries
Should always be considered serious and left to a veterinarian. If the animal will permit it, cover with a clean, moist dressing.

Hypothermia
The most common injury in floods (Heath 1999). It is treated more or less the same way as in humans: the animal is evacuated to a warm, dry place, dried off and if necessary given supplemental heat from an outside source like a heater. Heath recommends using a "hot box;" a small enclosure heated by an electric fan heater to warm a hypothermic animal. More advanced protocols are available, but should be administered by a veterinarian. Watch animals for hypothermia after decontamination.

Evacuation

The larger an animal is, the more effort required to evacuate it.

Dogs
- Handle alert, ambulatory dogs as described in previous chapters.
- Dogs that are unconscious or unable to rise may have to be either moved to a safer location or evacuated.
- Small dogs can be lifted and placed in a carrier. Support the dog on its side and place it gently in the carrier. Restrain and muzzle it. Wear heavy gloves to avoid bites.
- Large dogs should be placed on a litter or stretcher. One can be improvised from a piece of plywood or something similar. Using a litter is safer for both dog and rescuers.
- Approach the dog from the back. Try to establish control of the head. Muzzle the dog if possible. Grasp the dog by the nape of the neck and loose skin on his back and slide him backward away from harm or onto the litter. Don't pull on

the legs or get in front of the dog, since this makes it easier for him to bite you.

- If the surface is smooth and you don't need to lift the dog, slide the dog with a large towel or rug. This also allows you to avoid direct contact.

Horses and other large animals:

- Under most circumstances, rescuers will not be able to physically move large non-ambulatory animals.
- Approach the animal from the back. Stay out of range of the horse's legs. Assess the animal's injuries and provide treatment as necessary.
- Ambulatory horses may be evacuated by trailer. However, you will need experienced horse handlers for this option.
- It is possible to sling load large animals by helicopter. This is, as always, a high-risk option requiring experienced crews in the air and experienced horse handlers on the ground. See Appendix J for more information.

Ten Tips to Help You Avoid Developing A Serious Zoonotic Illness

Reprinted with permission from Animal Sheltering Magazine.

1. Stay current on your appropriate vaccinations, particularly tetanus and rabies.
2. Wash your hands frequently with antibacterial soap, especially after handling any animal and prior to eating and smoking.
3. Wear long pants and sturdy shoes or boots—no sandals or shorts.
4. Use gloves (preferably disposable) when changing litter pans, washing food and water dishes, or cleaning up feces, urine or vomit.
5. Disinfect scratches and bite wounds thoroughly.
6. Do not allow animals to lick your face or any wounds.
7. Learn safe and humane animal handling techniques and use proper equipment.
8. Seek assistance when handling animals whose dispositions are questionable.
9. Report any bites or injuries to your supervisor and to your physician.
10. Tell your physician that you work closely with animals, and visit her or him regularly.

Animal rescue and handling equipment

Wear your river PPE around large animals, including helmets. This provides extra physical protection.

Leashes, halters, etc.
Use a species-specific leash or halter to lead an animal if one is available. A leash for dogs or an adjustable halter for horses works better than trying to improvise something on the spot. Many animals (e.g. dogs and horses), are accustomed to these and are more easily controlled with something familiar.

Muzzles
Essential for dogs, handy if available for cats. Remember not to muzzle a panting dog or cat. TIP: A muzzle can be improvised from surgical tubing.

Improvise a temporary muzzle by using a couple of wraps from the dog's leash.

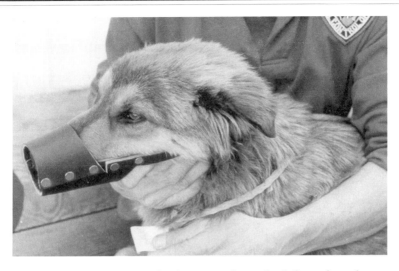

A manufactured muzzle fits better and can be left on for a longer period of time.

Catch poles

This is a pole with a noose on the end. The noose is slipped over the animal's head and tightened to capture it. This allows the rescuer to stay at a safe distance and the pole prevents the animal from coming at you.

A catch pole provides positive control.

TIP: You can make an improvised catch pole from a firefighting pike pole. Drill two holes a few inches apart in the handle end. Then thread a piece of rope knotted at one end through the holes.

Nets

Throw net
A open mesh net that can be thrown over small animals for quick capture.

Capture net
A net on a pole (similar to a butterfly net but larger). A small animal is scooped up in the net and then transferred to a cage or pen.

Tools of the trade (left to right): a capture net, a catch pole, grasper, and gloves.

Graspers
A padded set of jaws mounted on a handle. This allows a rescuer to humanely grasp the animal's neck and push it down to the ground, pinning the animal prior to capture.

A grasper can be used to control small animals.

Cages, pens, carriers, bags and sacks
- Put small captured animals in a sack, bag, or carrier for evacuation to a holding facility. Make sure the animal can breathe and that the sack is strong enough to hold it.
- Transfer the animal as soon as possible to a holding facility with adequate food and water. Decontaminate the animal first.
- Choose a pen or enclosure large enough, if possible, to allow the animal to stand and groom itself.

Animal PFDs
Commercial PFDs are available for medium to large dogs. TIP: a dog PFD can be improvised from a human PFD. Slide it over the dog's front legs and zip it down his back.

Working with professionals
Identify and establish a working relationship before the incident.

Veterinarians
- Identify vets who are willing to help beforehand as part of the disaster preplan. Make an alert roster with phone numbers and update it yearly.
- Include them in disaster drills and planning.
- Give vets some basic training in swiftwater (e.g. self-rescue) so that they can safely make "house calls."

Animal welfare and control
- Conduct joint training with rescue agencies so that animal welfare personnel have enough knowledge of swiftwater to keep themselves safe and make simple rescues (1st Responder) and know when to call in backup.
- Establish holding facilities for animals rescued during floods.

Rescue Agencies
- Establish a program to give rescuers some prior experience in animal handling experience and medical treatment.
- Train with animal control personnel.
- Establish working relationship with area veterinarians.

Appendix A

Swiftwater Rescue Site Checklist

__Establish incident command.

__Establish personnel accountability.

__Exclude all persons not having business at the rescue site.
  All rescuers must have proper PPE.

__Call for backup or mutual aid as necessary.

__Call for special equipment like wreckers, fire apparatus,
  or helicopters.

__Set an upstream spotter to provide warning of hazards such as
  trees floating down into the accident site and when necessary
  to halt all river traffic.

__Establish downstream safety: throw bags, boats, or a combination.
  DO NOT let a victim get downstream of the last rescue system.

__Select a rescue team according to the abilities of the team
  members.

__Make a rescue plan. How long will it take? What equipment
  and how many people do you need? How dangerous is it to
  the rescuers?

__Make a backup rescue plan in case the first plan fails or is not
  feasible. If the situation permits, set up the backup while
  trying the primary.

Appendix B

River hand and whistle signals for rescuers

Stop! **Go to this Side.**

OK to Proceed. **OK Are You OK?**

When in the water

I need help! **I'm OK**

Whistle Signals

One blast—Attention!

Three long blasts repeated—Emergency

Appendix C

Organizations

The American Humane Association Emergency Animal Relief
63 Inverness Drive
Englewood, CO 80112-5117
303-792-9900
www.americanhumane.org
The American Humane Association has helped to develop swiftwater animal rescue courses.

Rescue 3 International
P.O. Box 519
Elk Grove, CA
1-800-45RESC(U)
www.rescue3.com
Rescue 3 teaches two levels of swiftwater animal rescue. The course was developed with the cooperation of the American Humane Association.

Code 3 Associates
P.O. Box 1128
Erie, Colorado 80516
303-652-2552
www.intrepid.net/~dodge/
Specialists in disaster response/ planning and animal rescue training.

Humane Society of the United States
2100 L Street NW
Washington, DC 20037
www.hsus.org

American Red Cross
For more information contact your local Red cross representative.

United Animal Nations
5892 South Land Park Drive
P.O. Box 188890
Sacramento, CA
916-429-2457
www.uan.org

C. SPECIALTIES, INC.
Post Office Box 68591
Indianapolis, Indiana 46268-0591
www.cspecialties.com/
(small animal products, animal control equipment)

Tomahawk Live Trap Company
PO Box 323 Tomahawk, WI 54487
Order 800-27A-TRAP
Fax 715-453-4326
www.livetrap.com/
(humane traps, animal control equipment)

The Ketch All Company
4149 Santa Fe Road #2
San Luis Obispo, California 93401
Phone: 805-543-7223
Fax: 805-543-7154
(The Original Animal Control Pole)
www.Ketch-All.com/

NACA-National Animal Control Association
P.O. Box 480851
Kansas City, MO 64148-0851
www.netplace.net/naca

SAWA-Society of Animal Welfare Administrators
600 E. Evans St. Suite 3-341
Denver, CO 80222
303-758-9811

Care for Disabled Animals /CDA Products
18385 Van Arsdale Road
Potter Valley, CA 95469
707-743-1300
Fax: 707-743-2530
Anderson Sling and related products

Center for Equine Health
School of Veterinary Medicine
University of California
One Shields Ave.
Davis, CA 95616-8589
www.vetmed.ucdavis.edu/ceh

Appendix D

Further Reading

Bechdel, Les and Ray, Slim, *River Rescue*, 3rd ed., Boston, MA: Appalachian Mountain Club 1998

Ray, Slim, *Swiftwater Rescue*, Asheville, NC: CFS Press 1997

Heath, Sebastian, *Animal Management in Disasters,* St. Louis: Mosby 1999

Appendix E

Pet Care in Disasters

PET OWNERS—BE PREPARED WITH A DISASTER PLAN!
The best way to protect your family from the effects of a disaster is to have a disaster plan. If you are a pet owner, that plan must include your pets. Being prepared can save their lives.

Different disasters require different responses. But whether the disaster is a hurricane or a hazardous spill, you may have to evacuate your home.

In the event of a disaster, if you must evacuate, the most important thing you can do to protect your pets is to evacuate them, too. Leaving pets behind, even if you try to create a safe place for them, is likely to result in their being injured, lost, or worse. So prepare now for the day when you and your pets may have to leave your home.

1 HAVE A SAFE PLACE TO TAKE YOUR PETS
Red Cross disaster shelters cannot accept pets because of states' health and safety regulations and other considerations. Service animals who assist people with disabilities are the only animals allowed in Red Cross shelters. It may be difficult, if not impossible, to find shelter for your animals in the midst of a disaster, so plan ahead. Do not wait until disaster strikes to do your research.

* Contact hotels and motels outside your immediate area to check policies on accepting pets and restrictions on number, size, and species. Ask if "no pet" policies could be waived in an emergency Keep a list of "pet friendly" places, including phone numbers, with other disaster information and supplies. If you have notice of an impending disaster, call ahead for reservations.

* Ask friends, relatives, or others outside the affected area whether they could shelter your animals. If you have more than one pet, they may be more comfortable if kept together, but be prepared to house them separately.

* Prepare a list of boarding facilities and veterinarians who could shelter animals in an emergency; include 24-hour phone numbers.

* Ask local animal shelters if they provide emergency shelter or foster care for pets in a disaster. Animal shelters may be overburdened caring for the animals they already have as well as those displaced by a disaster, so this should be your last resort.

2 ASSEMBLE A PORTABLE PET DISASTER SUPPLIES KIT
Whether you are away from home for a day or a week, you'll need essential supplies. Keep items in an accessible place and store them in sturdy containers that can be carried easily (duffle bags, covered trash containers, etc.). Your pet disaster supplies kit should include:

* Medications and medical records (stored in a waterproof container) and a first aid kit.

* Sturdy leashes, harnesses, and/or carriers to transport pets safely and ensure that your animals can't escape.

* Current photos of your pets in case they get lost.

* Food, potable water, bowls, cat litter/pan, and can opener.

* Information on feeding schedules, medical conditions, behavior problems, and the name and number of your veterinarian in case you have to foster or board your pets.

* Pet beds and toys, if easily transportable.

3 KNOW WHAT TO DO AS A DISASTER APPROACHES
Often, warnings are issued hours, even days, in advance. At the first hint of disaster, act to protect your pet.

* Call ahead to confirm emergency shelter arrangements for you and your pets.

* Check to be sure your pet disaster supplies are ready to take at a moment's notice.

* Bring all pets into the house so that on won't have to search for them if you have to leave in a hurry.

* Make sure all dogs and cats are wearing collars and securely fastened, up-to-date identification. Attach the phone number and address of your temporary shelter, if you know it, or of a friend or relative outside the disaster area. You can buy temporary tags or put adhesive tape on the back of your pet's ID tag, adding information with an indelible pen.

You may not be home when the evacuation order comes. Find out if a trusted neighbor would be willing to take your pets and meet you at a prearranged location. This person should be comfortable with your pets, know where your animals are likely to be, know where your pet disaster supplies kit is kept, and have a key to your home. If you use a petsitting service, they may be available to help, but discuss the possibility well in advance.

Planning and preparation will enable you to evacuate with your pets quickly and safely. But bear in mind that animals react differently under stress. Outside your home and in the car, keep dogs securely leashed. Transport cats in carriers. Don't leave animals unattended anywhere they can run off. The most trustworthy pets may panic, hide, try to escape, or even bite or scratch. And, when you return home, give your pets time to settle back into their routines. Consult your veterinarian if any behavior problems persist.

CARING FOR BIRDS IN AN EMERGENCY

Birds should be transported in a secure travel cage or carrier. In cold weather, wrap a blanket over the carrier and warm up the car before placing birds inside. During warm weather, carry a plant mister to mist the birds' feathers periodically. Do not put water inside the carrier during transport. Provide a few slices of fresh fruits and vegetables with high water content. Have a photo for identification and leg

62

bands. If the carrier does not have a perch, line it with paper towels and change them frequently. Try to keep the carrier in a quiet area. Do not let the birds out of the cage or carrier.

ABOUT OTHER PETS
REPTILES Snakes can be transported in a pillowcase but they must be transferred to more secure housing when they reach the evacuation site. If your snakes require frequent feedings, carry food with you. Take a water bowl large enough for soaking as well as a heating pad. When transporting house lizards, follow the same directions as for birds.

POCKET PETS Small mammals (hamsters, gerbils, etc.) should be transported in secure carriers suitable for maintaining the animals while sheltered. Take bedding materials, food bowls, and water bottles.

A FINAL WORD
If you must evacuate do not leave your animals behind. Evacuate them to a prearranged safe location if they cannot stay with you during the evacuation period. (Remember, pets are not allowed in Red Cross shelters.) If there is a possibility that disaster may strike while you are out of the house, there are precautions you can take to increase your pets' chances of survival, but they are not a substitute for evacuating with your pets. For more information, contact The Humane Society of the United States, Disaster Services, 2100 L Street, N.W., Washington, DC 20037.

From "Pets and Disaster: Get Prepared," used with the permission of The Humane Society of the United States and the American Red Cross. For a free single copy of the "Pets and Disaster" brochure, send a stamped, self-addressed business-size envelope to The HSUS at the above address.

Appendix F

Suggested Breed Types and Coat Color Descriptions

Descriptor	Species	
	Cat	Dog
Breed	Domestic short hair	Labrador
		German Shepherd
	Domestic long hair	Chow
	Siamese	Poodle
	Burmese	Terrier
	Manx	Setter
	Other	Hound
Size	Not appropriate	Miniature
		Toy
		Small
		Medium
		Large
		Giant
Coat color	Solid black	Solid black
	Solid white	Solid white
	Solid gray	Solid gray
	Black and white	Black and white
	Gray and white	Tricolor
	Gray tabby	Light brown
	Orange tabby	Dark brown
	Calico	
Coat length	Short	Short
	Long	Long

Use of additional or more specific descriptions is likely to lead to confusion.

From Heath, *Animal Management in Disasters*, 1999.
Used with permission.

Appendix G

Pet population estimates

Percentage of households owning a pet		Number of pets per household
Dogs	36.5%	1.52
Cats	30.9%	1.95
Birds	5.7%	2.16

To get an estimated pet population figure, multiply the percentage of households with pets times the number of pets per household times the number of households (not the population) of the target area.

Thus, for a hypothetical county of 100,000 households, there are:

36.5% X 1.52 X 100,000 = 55,480 dogs
30.0% X 1.95 X 100,000 = 60,255 cats
 5.7% X 2.16 X 100,000 = 12,312 birds

Based, with permission, on 1992 American Veterinary Association studies cited in Heath, *Animal Management in Disasters*, 1999.

Appendix H

Disaster preparation for horses

- Develop a disaster plan—where would you take your horses in case evacuation were necessary? Plan for an alternate exit on foot with your horses if trailer access is blocked. Discuss the plan with everyone on the farm or at the stables so that every one knows what to do. There won't be time to figure it out during the disaster.
- Post the phone numbers of your local animal control services and the County Office of Emergency Services on your barn.
- Keep a First Aid kit for simple wounds available at all times. Include bandage material for lower legs and foot wrap, scissors, flashlight, duct tape, and phenylbutazone for pain. Work with your veterinarian to decide what to stock in your horse's first aid kit.
- Make sure that all your horse transporting equipment is ready to be used on a moment's notice and be sure your horses are well schooled in trailer and/or van loading.
- Keep a halter and lead rope readily available for every horse. There won't be time for a return trip.
- Take photographs of your horses and prepare written descriptions of each of them. Put these in a safe place, such as a bank safe deposit box, away from where the horses are kept, so that you can provide identification information to animal control personnel should your horses become lost or separated from you in a disaster.
- Place identification tags on all small animals.
- Maintain your property—remove any rolls of loose wire or dangerous debris that could cause entanglement.
- If you are evacuated, place an identification tag on the horse itself with the horse's name, your name, address and phone number. Cattle ear tags can be secured around the horse's neck and the information written with an indelible ink pen, or write the information on a piece of duct tape and place it on the halter.

- Meet your neighbors. In a disaster, you will all need to help each other.
- Volunteer your services with the local rescue organizations and shelters.
- In past disasters, it was noted that many of the horses at the shelters were also suffering from neglect (no or poor hoof care, malnutrition) or had chronic, untreated conditions that had no relation to the disaster (laminitis, abscessed teeth, recurrent uveitis). Every horse deserves routine veterinary and farrier care.

Reprinted with permission from *The Horse Report*, University of California, Davis, Center for Equine Health.

Appendix I

Treating critical horse injuries before the vet arrives

Severe lacerations with bleeding:

- Using a clean dressing, apply pressure with your hand directly over the source of bleeding.
- Gently clean the wound with a cold water hose only if it is severely contaminated by dirt and other debris.
- Do not apply any medication, disinfectant or ointments to any wound that may require suturing because these may cause tissue damage that can interfere with the suturing procedure. As a general rule, the less done to the wound before presentation to the veterinarian for suturing the better.
- If the horse will be transported to a veterinary clinic or if there will be a delay before the veterinarian arrives, apply a clean pressure bandage directly over the wound. Use plenty of padding between the injury and the bandaging material. Elastikon and/or Vet-wrap should be applied firmly enough to lessen bleeding but not so firmly as to cut off circulation. Always leave some of the padding material showing at the top and bottom of your wrap. Tourniquets are not recommended for use by untrained personnel.

Limb fractures or injuries with instability:

- Stabilize the injured limb in the first few minutes following the occurrence of a severe orthopedic injury. This will prevent further injury to the affected limb and its blood supply and will reduce the pain experienced by the animal.
- If a commercially designed splint is not available, you can make one with a pillow and several rolls of Elastikon tape or Vet-wrap type bandages. Wrap the pillow around the leg and

apply the tape pulling the pillow as tight as you can while wrapping. After several rolls of tape have been applied, the bandage will become very stiff, thereby stabilizing the leg. This is only a short-term solution which will need to be replaced with more permanent stabilization as soon as possible.

- When using tranquilizers in a severely injured horse, use a very low dose. These animals easily fall into shock and higher doses of tranquilizers can compound low blood pressure complications.

Reprinted with permission from *The Horse Report*, University of California, Davis, Center for Equine Health.

Appendix J

The Anderson Sling

Charles Anderson, a welder from Potter Valley, California, and founder of Care for Disabled Animals, designed a specialized equine sling that has been used successfully for helicopter short hauling of stranded or injured animals. He designed the sling after consultation with Dr. John Madigan and Richard Morgan of the UC Davis School of Veterinary Medicine.

The Anderson Sling was used to rescue a group of mules and a horse who were stranded in heavy snow near the Dodge Ridge Ski Resort in California in November 1991. This was a good test situation since the animals were not injured, the overhead access was clear and the weather conditions were mild. By the end of the day, all the animals had been successfully airlifted four miles to solid ground using the sling. Since then, it has been used to rescue a horse stranded on the rocky cliffs above the American River in 1992 (featured on the television show Rescue 911) and to rescue two foals and four adult horses in the flooded areas in Southern California in 1993.

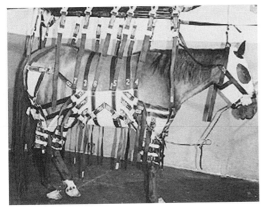

What makes the sling unique is its support system. In the past, equine slings did not support the horse evenly, lifting mostly from the abdomen. Many horses were uncomfortable with this lack of support and would panic, often jumping and twisting themselves free. The Anderson Sling supports the horse from the skeletal system, distributing the horse's support and restraint system. Because the head and neck constitute a good portion of the horse's body weight, the sling helps steady the horse, preventing the jumping and twisting that occurred with earlier slings. The Anderson Sling also has considerable padding and leg supports to keep the sling in place and make it more comfortable for the animal. In addition to rescue, the sling has been used for long term rehabilitation of horses unable to stand.

The Anderson Sling is available in various sizes to the public and to rescue organizations. However, *organizations should not attempt helicopter short hauls without adequate prior training, as well the support of experienced horse handlers.* See Appendix C.

For more information on short hauls, see the author's *Swiftwater Rescue,* listed in the Appendix D.

Adapted with permission from *The Horse Report*, University of California, Davis Center of Equine Health.

Index